TIME MANAGEMENT

LEARNING SUPPORT SERVICES

Please return
on or before
the last date
stamped below

City College NORWICH

A FINE WILL BE CHARGED FOR OVERDUE ITEMS

Other titles in the Lifeskills Personal Development series:

Assertiveness – A Positive Process
Communication – Time to Talk
Preparing for Successful Learning
Relationships – A Question of Quality
Stress, Health and Your Lifestyle
Successful Learning in Action
Transitions – The Challenge of Change

TIME MANAGEMENT

Conquer the Clock

Dr Barrie Hopson
and Mike Scally

MERCURY

Copyright © 1988, 1991 Lifeskills Communications Ltd

First published in 1988 by Lifeskills Publishing Group
New Edition published in 1992
by Mercury Books
Gold Arrow Publications Ltd
862 Garratt Lane, London SW17 0NB

Reprinted December 1992

Drawings by Kate Charlesworth

Typeset by Phoenix Photosetting, Chatham, Kent

Printed and bound in Great Britain by
Dotesios Ltd, Trowbridge, Wiltshire.

British Library Cataloguing in Publication Data is available

ISBN 1–85252–116–3

Foreword

Dear Reader,

Welcome to our series of open learning workbooks! In this brief foreword, we invite you to consider some of our beliefs:

- We do not need teachers to learn! Most of what we know in life was not learned in school, college or formal education. We can, and do, learn in a whole range of ways and we learn best when we know our own needs.

- The best way to help people is to encourage them to help themselves. Self-help and self-management avoid the dependency which blocks development and burdens ourselves and others.

- Awareness, knowledge and skills give us more options in life. Lack of any of these is a disadvantage; possession of them allows us to live fuller lives, shaping events rather than simply reacting.

- The more able and accomplished we become, the more we fill society's reservoir of talent and contribute to the common good.

- It has been said that the future is not what it used to be! In this age, the goalposts keep being moved, so increasingly our security needs to come from having information and skills.

The term 'lifeskill' came from work based on these beliefs which we began at Leeds University in the 1970s. Our philosophy has been widely applied in education, in industry and commerce, and in the community, inviting people to take charge of their lives and make them satisfying and rewarding.

Lifeskills have so far been available through training courses and teaching programmes. *Now* they are available in a self-help format consistent with the Lifeskills approach because *you* are in charge of your own learning. Learn at your own pace, in your own time, and apply your learning to your situation. We wish you both enjoyment and success!

Barrie Hopson

Mike Scally

November 1991

Before You Start...

This workbook has been written for people wanting to know more about personal self-development. It is about reading and doing, so we have chosen to write it as an open learning workbook.

What is open learning? Open learning is a term used to describe a study programme which is very flexibly designed so that it adapts to the needs of individual learners. Some open learning programmes involve attendance at a study centre of some kind, or contact with a tutor or mentor, but even then attendance times are flexible and suit the individual. This workbook is for you to use at home or at work and most of the activities are for you to complete alone. We sometimes suggest that it would be helpful to talk with a friend or colleague – self development is easier if there is another person with whom to talk over ideas. But this isn't essential by any means.

With this workbook you can:

- organise your study to suit your own needs

- study the material alone or with other people

- work through the book at your own pace

- start and finish just where and when you want to, although we have indicated some suggested stopping points with a ☕ symbol.

The sections marked Personal Project involve you in more than working through the text. They require you to take additional time – sometimes an evening, sometimes a week. For this reason, we are not giving clear guidelines on how long it will take you to complete this workbook, but the written part of the book will probably take you about six hours to complete.

Contents

Introduction: What Is Time Management?

- 'I'd really like to go swimming on Thursday, but I'm afraid I simply haven't got the time.'

- 'Yes, I'd love to start that new project, but I've got a thousand and one things to finish first.'

- 'I'm sorry to break our date, but I really must complete that report for tomorrow morning.'

- 'Perhaps we could meet two weeks on Wednesday – that's the first free day I have.'

Do the above statements sound familiar? If you find yourself talking like this too often, then you really need to make some changes and conquer the clock!

Time management is about setting clear priorities for yourself and making sure you achieve them. It recognises that time is a limited resource – so we have to make choices. Above all, it recognises time is a wasting resource: when it's gone it's gone! We need to know how to conquer the clock now.

We hope that by the end of this workbook you will no longer think to yourself, 'I would like to do that but I haven't got the time.' You will either arrange to do it, or think, 'I could do that but I like what I'm doing a lot better!'

Three key words can help you achieve better management of your time. They are:

Knowledge
Choice
Time

- You need to Know clearly what you need or want to do.
- You need to make a Choice about which of these to do.
- You need to arrange a Time to act on your choice.

The important skill that this programme emphasises is your ability to crystallise priorities and to apportion time to achieve them. It offers you the opportunity to explore techniques for planning your time more effectively so that you can accomplish all your important priorities, some of your less important priorities and even a few of the relatively unimportant ones.

We realise that life is full of unexpected surprises, so another important element in this programme is flexibility. Indeed, this workbook itself is flexible: you choose when and how you use it. By the end of the book we hope you will be able to choose and use your time more efficiently.

Objectives

- To help you become aware of how you presently use your time.

- To help you identify priorities in the way you use your time.

- To show you how to rank your priorities in order of importance.

- To introduce you to the concept of sold time, maintenance time and discretionary time.

- To develop your skills in managing time.

Managing time is not about always being busy!

We are not suggesting that every minute of your time must be packed with activity, but that it is possible to get what you want out of as much time as possible. That includes planning for relaxation.

Time Management Is About Priorities

↓

Priorities Result From Setting Objectives

↓

Setting Objectives Is About Planning

↓

Planning Is About Control

↓

Being In Control Is Being Self-empowered

↓

Self-empowered People Manage Their Time.

What Would you Like to get from this Workbook?

Before you move on to the first section, take about five minutes to clarify what you would like to achieve by doing this workbook, and what you hope to get out of it.

Note down three things you find frustrating about the way you spend your time at the moment (e.g. are you often late? do you find it difficult to get certain things done? do you feel all your time belongs to other people?).

1 ....

2 ....

3 ....

Now let your imagination loose for a few minutes to think about the next questions, and the possibilities that you could open up for yourself. What are your personal objectives in doing this workbook?

Look back over your thoughts and ideas, then write down your objectives below:

One important thing I would really like to achieve that I don't have time for at the moment:

....

....

Two things I would like to change about the way I spend my time at the moment:

....

....

....

....

Now that you have begun to identify your personal goals, we suggest you keep returning to what you have written in the above space as you go through the workbook. Reviewing your objectives regularly will help you to monitor your progress. It will also help you to choose the time management techniques that are most helpful to you. Don't hesitate to change or add to your objectives as you work through the sections – your ideas will change with your progress!

Section One: Life Investment Record

The objective of this section is to help you become aware of how you *actually* spend your time.

The key to time management is knowing how to spend your time. You have 24 hours available each day. Regard them as a stock of investment funds – where you invest them decides what return you will get on the day.

First, it is important to find out how you *really* spend your time. This will provide you with basic information which will help you make your time choices later on in the workbook. You can do this by investing some of your time in preparing a Life Investment Record. This records your activities for every hour in your week.

Personal Project

The following Life Investment Record splits the days of the week into two-hour periods. We suggest you fill in the record over the next seven days. You will need to complete a week's 24-hour Life Investment Record before you can really begin to tackle the other sections in this programme.

We have found two-hour blocks to be a happy medium, but you can split the chart into whatever time periods suit you, although these should not be too large. For example someone who doesn't work full time might want more space for daytime activities compared with someone who does have a full-time job.

Every night before you go to sleep, enter into the record what you did during the day. It is important to make your entries regularly each day, because we can very quickly forget what we have done.

Life Investment Record

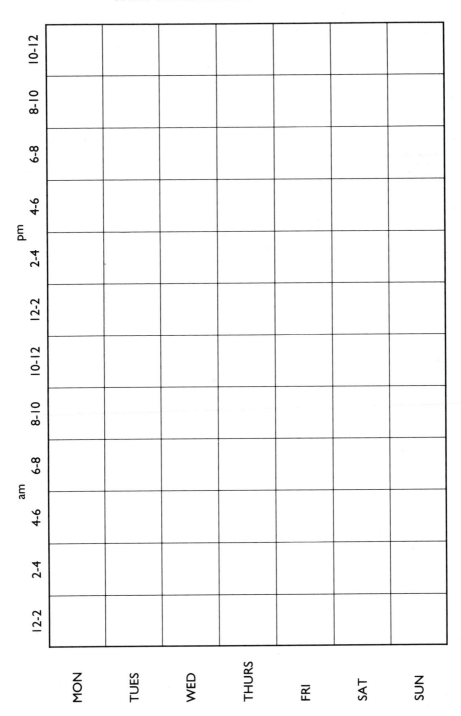

You may find it helpful to keep a Time Diary, jotting down things as you do them during the day. You will still need to transfer your entries on to the Life Investment Record at the end of the week, to give an overview of how you spent your time. An overview is very important, as it will allow you to look back and identify patterns in the way you use your time.

When you have completed your Life Investment Record for a week you are in a position to go on to analyse how your time was spent.

In the chart below, make a list of the activities described in your Life Investment Record – sleeping, eating, watching TV, cooking, etc. If you do paid work you may find it useful to break down how you spend your time at work. Use sub-headings for your different work activities, for example, telephone calls, meetings, photocopying, travelling.

A few common activities are already listed; fill in the others from your personal record. Next, work out how many hours you spent on each activity. Mark this figure in the space provided against each activity.

Activity Chart	
Activity	**No. of Hours Spent**
Eating	
Childcare	
Sleeping	
Travelling	
Shopping	
Domestic Chores	
Cooking	
Working	

Spend a few moments looking over your chart. Now rank in order your activity hours in the table on the next page. Against 1, put the activity with the highest number of hours, against 2 the next highest, and so on.

Activity	Amount of Time Spent
1	
2	
3	
4	
5	
6	
7	
8	
9	
10	
11	
12	
13	
14	
15	
16	
17	
18	
19	
20	

Look over your chart and think about the following questions:

What surprises you about the way you have spent your week?

....

....

Was there anything unusual about your week?

....

....

What return are you getting on your investment; how satisfied are you?

....

....

What changes would you like to make?

....

....

....

Can you see ways of saving time so you could invest in something else? If so, what are they?

....

....

....

Are there any gaps where you cannot recall what you were doing?

....

Summary

You now have an analysis of how you actually spent a week of your life. It may well have produced some surprises for you! For example, the amount of time spent watching the television, or walking the dog might be much greater than you thought. Maybe you spent less time on the briefcase full of 'homework' papers than you thought! Even if your Life Investment Record turned out as you expected, there will be opportunities for you to spend more time on some activities and less on others.

The next section will look at your Life Investment Record in more detail, so you can start identifying areas where you could save time or might put it to better use.

You Will Never Have That Week Again. Was It A Good Way Of Spending Your Time?

Section Two: Time Check

The objectives of this section are:

- to increase your awareness of how you now spend your time;

- to develop your skills and techniques in managing time.

Our lives are constantly changing. We develop as individuals, our interests diversify, and the circumstances around us alter. As a result, we need regularly to review our use of time, to ensure that what we do actually accords with what we want to do.

Use the questionnaire below to review your use of time last week.

My Use of Time Last Week

Overall impressions of how I
have spent the week.

How much time have I given to
what I enjoy?

How much time have I spent
on what I don't enjoy?

Have I wasted time?
How much? How?

How much time was given to
what I think is important?

Did I use time spent waiting or
travelling constructively?

How much time did I allocate
to my priorities?

How organised was I each day
in knowing what I wanted to
achieve?

continued

Did anything not get done that I
wished had been done,
because I put it off until another
time?

Have I used any time particularly successfully this week? Can
I build on this next week?

Have I spent time on routines
or habits I would like to break?

Have I given myself a reward
for time well spent?

Have I set myself some
deadlines and met them?

Have I wasted other people's
time? If so, how?

Have I found time to relax?

Have I asked frequently;
'What's the best use of my time
right now?

What does the above tell you about how you used your time last week?

....

....

....

Is there anything you might want to change next week?

....

....

....

Personal Project: Weekly Time Checks

Try doing a time check review every week. We have included the daily work chart of one of our staff, so you can see the sort of things to include. This chart is especially helpful if you work, but you should also include time spent outside working hours. If you don't work, or work part time, it's still worth filling in a time check chart to assess your progress towards conquering the clock!

Daily Time Charts	
Time	**Activity**
8.50	Cup of tea. Searched for missing letter—did some filing too.
9.25	Couple of people wanting to talk.
9.35	begin meeting with Mike on posters to accompany a book—it's hard to grasp and tease out what we want.
10.05	Typesetter arrives – we all 3 look at boards
10.35	Publishing team meeting-followed by 'debriefing' session with M.D.
11.50	Cup of coffee, chat with Annmarie. Karen's poorly so sent her home!
12.30	Back to poster meeting and reading typeset boards.
1.00	Continue poster concept meeting in pub
1.45	pick up boards again
2.15	Barrie rang, leaving messages, etc.
2.35	Skim read 2 magazines (HRD Quarterly, Training Tomorrow)
2.50	Photocopy our drafts and ideas for poster. Start lay out.
3.50	Designs for new catalogue cover arrive. Peter, Michael and I look at them.
4.05	Mike briefs me on publication schedule of NOW books.
4.30	Make 2 phone calls. Then we all get together for a drink to celebrate 2 birthdays.
5.00	Return to layout for 20 minutes. Write out tasks for tomorrow.
5.45	Leave.

It's a good idea to keep your weekly time checks together so you can review your progress and identify recurring features. Later on we shall look at the techniques of using a time management diary or planner. This has many uses, but for the moment it is worth noting that it is an ideal place to keep your time checks.

Summary

In this section you began to think about how you really use your time. Section Three will let you go into more detail and find out about how to plan to use time for the things you enjoy.

Section Three: Time And Satisfaction

The objectives of this section are:

- to help you become aware of how you presently spend your time;

- to help you identify priorities in the ways you use your time.

In this section we look at the central time management problem. That is how well we match what we want to do with what we actually do. The aim is to increase the time you spend on satisfying activities as a proportion of all time spent.

To do this you need to know how you *really* spend your time now, and how you would spend your time to give you the greatest satisfaction and pleasure. Let's look at a technique for doing this.

What Do You Find Satisfying Now?

In the space below make a list of the activities that satisfy you. Define satisfaction entirely in your own terms, but you must only use activities that you actually do now. This will vary greatly between individuals. For some, the pain and exertion of climbing mountains is worth the satisfaction of reaching the top. Others regard the enjoyment of each moment for itself as outweighing any ultimate goal. So make your list one which shows what actually satisfies you, not what you think you ought to do.

Satisfying Activities

A pie chart can show the activities that satisfy you and it also shows the relative satisfaction you get from each activity. Everyone's Satisfaction Pie is different; look at the two examples! Yours will probably contain many activities that are different from these examples.

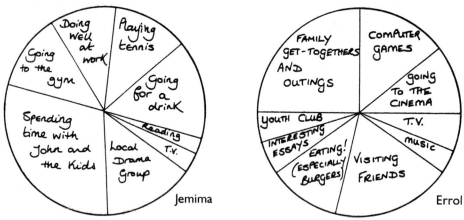

Jemima

Errol

Now mark your satisfying activities on the pie chart below as slices of the pie – the more satisfying the activity, the larger its slice of the pie. The complete pie is the sum of your total life satisfactions.

One thing the pie chart makes clear is that you can only increase the time you devote to one satisfying activity at the expense of time devoted to another activity. This means you have to make choices.

Your Satisfaction Pie

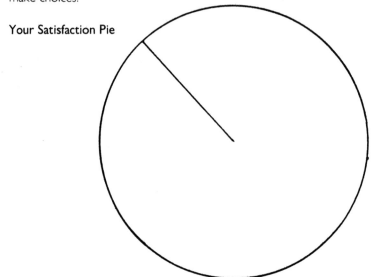

Spend a moment or two looking at your Satisfaction Pie and then go on to the next stage. This looks at the amount of time you actually spend on each of your satisfying activities.

How Much Time Do You Spend Now on Satisfying Activities?

We have shown you Jemima's and Errol's Satisfaction Pies. Here is how their Time Pies look:

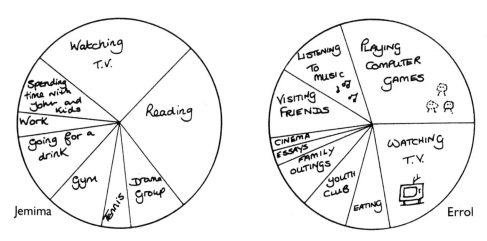

Like many of us, they both watch more television than the satisfaction they get from that activity warrants! On the Time Pie below enter the amount of time you now spend on your satisfying activities. Again you should show the amount of time spent by the size of the slice.

Your Time Pie

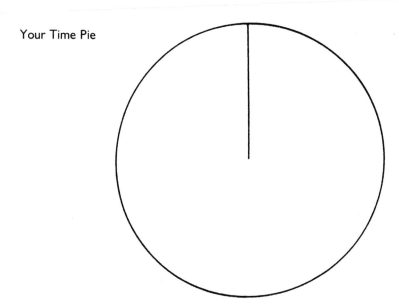

Compare your two pies and answer these questions:

Does anything surprise you about either of your Pies?

....

....

....

....

Are there any differences between your Satisfaction Pie and your Time Pie? What are they?

....

....

....

....

What does this say about the way you are living your life now?

....

....

....

....

If you look back and compare the Satisfaction and Time Pies in our example, you can see some clear mismatches between the two. Many of the things that Jemima and Errol really enjoy and find satisfying are squeezed out by other activities.

Look back at your Life Investment Record in Section One and compare it with your two Pies. Then spend about five minutes on the next two questions.

Are there any other satisfying activities in your Life Investment Record that you have forgotten to include in your Satisfaction Pie? Jot down some thoughts in the box below:

Your Time Pie shows the amount of time you *think* you spend on satisfying activities. Your Life Investment Record shows the amount of time you *actually* spent on those activities over one week. Is there any mismatch between the time you think you spend and the time you actually spend on satisfying activities? Jot down some thoughts here:

Summary: Pies in The Skies!

We have been asking you to focus on activities you do now that you find satisfying. In the final part of this section, we invite you to use your imagination! In an ideal world, how would you spend your time? Below you will find a final set of pies. Using the same headings as in your original set of pies, fill in the Satisfaction Pie as you would like it to look and the Time Pie as you would like it to look.

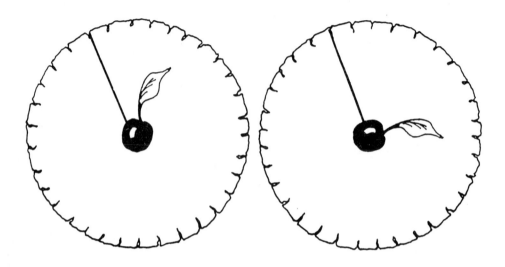

Your Ideal Satisfaction Pie   Your Ideal Time Pie

By comparing your actual and your ideal sets of pies, you now know where you are and where you would like to be. You have the basic information for making time management decisions which will enable you to manage your time to your greater satisfaction.

Today is the first day of the rest of your life – so make the most of it!

Section Four: Identifying Priorities

The objectives of this section is to help you identify priorities in the way you use your time.

No matter who we are, we only have twenty-four hours in a day. Our time is limited but the possible demands on it are infinite. If we are not simply to react to demands, we have to choose how we allocate our time. To do this we have to identify our priorities. In the last section you analysed how you spent your time last week. In this section, we give you the opportunity to consider how you will spend your time next week.

In the space below, note down all the ideas that occur to you in response to the questions. Spend about three minutes on each question. Don't try to put your answers in any order; simply note down your ideas freely as they occur to you.

What I Have To Do Next Week

What I Want To Do Next Week

Take each list in turn and pick out the six most important items that you have to do, or want to do next week.

When you have done this, look over the twelve items you have picked out. Ask yourself which of these items you are going to give most priority to. Think through all the factors, the implications, the pros and cons of each item and decide which will be your number one choice. Write this choice against 1 in the space below and then repeat the process for 2,3,4, and so on.

Priorities For This Week

1

2

3

4

5

6

7

8

9

10

11

12

Now that you've drawn up your list of priorities, you may find it helpful to copy it out and keep it somewhere where you will see it frequently during the next week.

Review the list two or three times during the week and strike off items when you've done them. You may find that some items are no longer priorities, that they have resolved themselves or changed. Your list will alter accordingly. What is left undone on the list at the end of the week can be included in the priorities you make for the following week.

At the end of next week, review your list of priorities, and answer the questions below. Use a friend or colleague as a consultant if you would find it helpful.

How aware am I of my priorities?

....

....

How much am I choosing/initiating?

....

....

Am I proactive or reactive? (Do I make things happen or let things happen to me?)

....

....

Summary

In this section we have looked at the principle of identifying priorities, and have begun to explore techniques for doing this. In the next section we will look at another useful technique for ranking priorities in order of importance.

Section Five: Effective List Making

The objective of this section is to look at techniques for ranking priorities in order of importance.

We all have important things to do in our lives, but how do we remember how and when to do them? Trusting to memory is one way, but unfortunately it is not very reliable. It also increases anxiety. Relying on someone else to remind you means handing over responsibility for your life to someone else – not very self-empowered behaviour! We would suggest that one satisfactory way of guaranteeing you achieve your priorities is by making an effective list.

Some people feel that list making is tedious, and one more way of wasting time rather than saving it. Below we suggest that you weigh up the advantages and disadvantages of list making for yourself. We've listed some advantages, but there's space for some of your own. By filling in your own lists of advantages and disadvantages you can quickly see which side outweighs the other.

List Making As A Tool For Time Management	
Advantages	Disadvantages
Takes away anxiety about forgetting to do things Having it on paper ensures that you don't forget Helps you work out what is important Provides an immediate progress report on what you have achieved	

Your disadvantages might have included that lists take too long to compile, they might not be comprehensive – and what happens if you lose your list! Despite these disadvantages, we still think that lists can really help you to manage your time, so here are some tips on effective list making.

Where To Start

We suggest you do this exercise at the end of the day, when you can start to plan ahead. Spend about five minutes considering what you'd like to achieve tomorrow. In the space below make a list of all the things you *have* to do tomorrow and all the things you *want* to do tomorrow.

Things I Have To Do Tomorrow:

....

....

....

Things I Want To Do Tomorrow:

....

....

....

Now work out your priorities by coding the items on the list into three categories:

A   Things you must do or want to do tomorrow.

B   Things you should do or would like to do by the end of the day.

C   Things you would quite like to do by the end of the day, but it won't matter if you don't.

Write your list in the box below, giving each item a letter code. Then number the item (A1, A2, etc.) according to how important they are.

Priorities List

As you go through your day, complete the A items first, then the Bs and finally the Cs. Try out this system every day for a week, making a new list for each day.

You may find that this way of planning doesn't exactly suit you, so there are some tips below which will give you some ideas for minor alterations. Feel free to adapt our Priorities List but don't forget that, however you do your list, unpleasant jobs still have to be done!

Personal Project

Bear in mind these tips during this trial week.

- Make your new list at the end of each day, while you're still thinking about tasks to do for tomorrow.

- Keep the list with you.

- Cross off items when they've been achieved. This acts as a reward.

- Ask yourself from time to time, 'Am I spending too much time on the B and C items?'

- As soon as something new occurs, add it to the list and letter code it.

- Have you got the right balance between what you must do and what you want to do? It's important to take care of some of your needs.

- Ask yourself periodically, 'Am I doing what I want to do right now?'

- Don't put off unpleasant jobs – they won't get any easier!

- When you've completed an A item that you must do, reward yourself by achieving one of your 'wants'.

- Transfer to tomorrow's list any uncompleted items from today.

- If a C item remains on your list for more than three or four days, decide to upgrade it to A or B, or cross it off and forget about it!

- Don't forget to build in 'thinking time' where necessary.

- Things like going to the shops or writing reports often take longer than you think, so build in extra time, say 20%, if you can.

- Use short C jobs to act as energisers, or do one at the beginning of the day to get off to a successful start.

Summary

At the end of your trial week, ask yourself these questions:

How does a list help me; how does it hinder me?

....
....
....
....

Did I forget anything?

....
....
....
....

Did I get more done? If so, why?

....
....
....
....

What did I do differently during the week I made lists?

....
....
....
....

You will almost certainly want to adapt your list making techniques to suit your personal needs. But if you persist you will find list making and prioritising a powerful tool in organising your time.

Section Six: Using a Diary or Planner

The objective of this section is to introduce you to a powerful time management aid.

As your time management skills have developed, you will be aware that you have produced a number of lists and charts. These are the basic tools with which you plan your time. As with any tools it helps to keep them all together and a good place to do this is in a diary, file or planner.

Diaries are familiar to us all. They provide a convenient place to keep your daily lists and are essential for forward planning. Not only that but they are relatively cheap and can be very cheerful. You may prefer to use something larger and more roomy – an A4 ringbinder file or box, for instance. These are great for storing lots of information, but not so effective for detailed forward planning.

Personal planners or organisers provide all the advantages of diaries plus extra space to keep records and charts. Planners need not be expensive; you can buy a notebook and customise it yourself. On the other hand, professionally produced planners are attractive and provide preprinted pages and charts. An advantage of many commercially available planners is their loose leaf binder system which allows you to add and reposition pages as you like.

A possible disadvantage of planners is their size. Some of them are quite bulky. If size is important to you, opt for a small, easily portable pocket diary for essential daily information and a larger notebook, held at home or work, for the longer term plans, charts and diagrams. You may find that you use a box file for home organising and a personal planner for work, or maybe a small diary would suffice if you put other information on an office wall chart. The important thing is to find something that suits you.

In the space below write down a list of items to keep in your diary.

What kinds of things did you put down? Was it just appointments or did you also list decisions that needed to be made? An advantage of listing decisions is that you can forget about them until, for example, 11.00 am Wednesday morning. You can use your time more constructively than worrying on and off for a few days about decisions you need to make.

There are examples of two diaries on the following pages. As you will see, the first diary is for a week and contains items relating to both home and work. The second diary is a daily one, and covers mainly work. It might make sense for you to keep more than one diary, especially if you have a busy working day and a busy social life. If you are very involved in something like a political party or social club you may want to keep a diary specifically for that.

Gather together all the charts and lists you have produced to plan your time. Sort them out into those that go in the diary section and those that go in the planner section. Enter them into the appropriate sections. Below is an example of how you could do this.

Diary	Planner
Priorities list for the week Monthly diary Weekly diary	Life Investment Record Activity percentages charts Satisfaction pies Time pies Use of time this week charts Yearly diary Quotes or aphorisms which encourage you

Use the space below to decide where you will store your lists and charts.

Weekly Diary: 7 November to 13 November

	Monday	Tuesday	Wednesday	Thursday	Friday	Saturday	Sunday
Morning	Prepared papers for afternoon meetings	Working at Home	Working at Home	Made beeswax polish and polished chairs	Off to a furniture shop in Warrington with George	Go into town with children for shoes →	Washing and Ironing
Afternoon	12-2 meeting 2-4 meeting	Working at Home	Lunch with Gill ↓	→	lunch with George travel back		Walk with my children and george and his children in Ilkley
Evening	Watched television	Made a meal for Christine - Chat	Stripped kitchen chairs & varnish	Late night shopping	Collapse and fall asleep in front of the T.V.	Prepared some delicious food from new book	Painted legs of kitchen chairs

Monday 15th October

Time		Action
7AM		**Talk to**
8AM		Mike — Review
9AM		Liz — Notes for presentation
PREPARE PRESENTATION 10AM		Dennis — ideas for new programme ?
11AM		
Phone Calls. NOON		**Telephone**
L U N C H 1PM		Lifeskills — Peter Gannon
PRESENTATION 2PM		Moira 2386
3PM		Book Squash Court
MIKE — Review Meeting 4PM		
DICTATION 5PM		**Write to**
6PM		Minutes — SPR Meeting (see PLANS)
Squash — Jerry. 7PM		Norman Smith re. bookings
8PM		
9PM		
10PM		**Notes**

October 1990
M T W T F S S
1 2 3 4 5 6 7
8 9 10 11 12 13 14
15 16 17 18 19 20 21
22 23 24 25 26 27 28
29 30 31

Notes

Pay Visa Bill

! Expenses

Order Stationery
— ohp pens
— 3 A4 pads
— 12 binders

Summary

Together, your diary and planner contain the techniques with which you can plan a more satisfying life. They can only help you if you actually use them. Arrange a definite time each week for your planning activities.

Section Seven: Creating An Efficient Working Environment

The objective of this section is to show you how an organised workspace, office or study can help you manage your time.

Although we use the words 'office' and 'desk' in this section, the principles of creating a good working environment apply just as well to a home. Think about the difference between working in a clean, well-organised kitchen and a messy, chaotic one. Household tasks need just as much organising as office work!

Imagine that you have an important job to do tomorrow. What would make you feel good about starting it? Jot down a few thoughts on how your ideal working environment would be.

Your Ideal Working Environment

We think the following things are important:

- A clear workspace or desk – this lets you concentrate fully on the task.

- Having the right tools for the job. Before you start make sure you have the right equipment, books, stationery, etc. Then you won't waste valuable time searching for things.

- Peace and quiet (if possible!). Don't start an important job when you know that someone is due to visit, the children are coming back from school, or when you know the telephone will be particularly busy.

- Having a comfortable workspace. You can't concentrate if you're thinking about your aching back or smarting eyes. Try to work in good light, sitting in a comfortable chair at a worksurface that is the right height.

- If you can, put a favourite picture on the wall or fresh flowers on your desk. When you take a break look at these, let your mind wander and relax.

Of course, you should try to be organised all the time, not just when you have an important job to do! Knowing exactly where things are can save hours.

The basis of a time efficient approach to many jobs is a good filing system. This isn't as technical as it sounds: most people 'file' their household goods, for example, cleaning materials in one cupboard, food in another. Filing can mean anything from putting all the bills in an old shoe box or storing holiday information in a scrap book, to the more complex filing systems found in offices.

Filing Systems

Think for a few minutes about the kinds of filing systems, if any, that you use at the moment. Jot them down in the space below:

....

....

....

....

....

....

....

....

....

One excellent way of keeping track of correspondence and information is to put it into different sections. If you are working you could try the following six categories; if you don't work you will probably find that two or three of these categories will be enough. Use files or boxes to keep each section separate.

| File | – This is material which is finished with but needs to be kept for reference. |

| Do now | – For letters, bills, etc. which need actioning today. |

| Do soon | – For jobs which must be done soon but are not yet urgent. |

| Read | – Papers, magazines and reports can go in here. |

| Pass on | – For information which needs to go to another person with some comment or advice from you. |

| Awaiting info | – For jobs which need further information before anything can be done. |

If the system works you will find that jobs progress through most or all of these files. For example, a paper comes in which you must read. You spot something which a friend or colleague would be interested in and put it in the 'do soon' file. Next day you move it to the 'do now' file and you write them a letter with a copy of the article, before putting the paper and copy letter into the 'awaiting information' file. Your friend writes back thanking you, so the letters and paper can now be filed.

In- and Out-trays

These can be very useful for keeping your mail all in one place. Do make sure that any incoming letters, messages or memos are put straight into the in-tray. Look at the in-tray regularly and, if necessary, transfer things to your filing system. When things are due to be posted or given straight to another person put them in the out-tray.

Notice boards

Notice boards are a great way of reminding yourself about things at home and at work – they also let family and colleagues know what is happening or what needs to be done. The other good thing about notice boards is that they can be as bright and colourful as you want. Being organised doesn't mean being dull!

- Before we move on, don't forget another very important place for putting some papers:

Some information is really not worth keeping. Each time you receive a piece of paper ask yourself, 'do I need to keep this?' – if you don't put it in the bin!

Summary

Now that we've gone through some ideas and tips, jot down any that you think you might use. Is there anything you can do right now to improve the way you organise things?

Section Eight: Sold Time, Maintenance Time and Discretionary Time

The objective of this section is to introduce you to the concept of Sold Time, Maintenance Time and Discretionary Time*.

Sold Time is the time that you sell to an employer. Or, as a student, the time you give to studying. It involves exchanging your time for money or for qualifications, which can be regarded as future money. Sold Time extends beyond the actual hours spent at work or college. It includes the time spent in preparation for these – preparation time, homework, travel time, etc.

Maintenance Time is the time spent keeping things ticking over. It is when you do the things that are necessary to maintain yourself – sleeping, eating, cleaning, dressing, etc. It also includes time spent maintaining others – cooking and cleaning for dependants and relations, family shopping, parents' evenings, etc.

Discretionary Time is the time that remains. It is the time when we can choose how we spend it. It is free time to spend as we like.

On the next pages, you will find three time charts, one for Sold Time, one for Maintenance Time and one for Discretionary Time. Fill them in for last week, using your Life Investment Record if necessary.

You will find that some activities are difficult to categorise. For example, cooking, bathing the children or shopping could all be maintenance time or discretionary time – it depends whether or not you enjoy them. Similarly, travelling to a job could be seen as sold or discretionary time. You decide how to categorise this sort of activity; you may even want to split the time between two sections.

Under each type of time, write down all your activities that fall into that category. Note down the amount of time you spend on each activity for each day of the week.

Add up the daily total for each type of time use in the Total line at the bottom of each chart. Finally add up the grand total for each type of time use.

---

* This classification of time was developed by Jack Loughary of the University of Oregon.

Sold Time Chart

	Mon	Tues	Wed	Thu	Fri	Sat	Sun
Total							
				Grand Total			

Maintenance Time Chart

	Mon	Tues	Wed	Thu	Fri	Sat	Sun
Total							
				Grand Total			

Discretionary Time Chart						
Mon	Tues	Wed	Thu	Fri	Sat	Sun
Total						
				Grand Total		

You should now have a clear picture of:

- Your weekly total for each activity.

- Your daily totals for the three different types of time.

- Your week's grand total for each type of time use.

Here is what one person's completed charts looked like.

Michael's Sold Time Chart						
Mon	Tues	Wed	Thu	Fri	Sat	Sun
7.40 - travel to work. 8.30 – 5.30 WORK Travel home – 40 mins. Work at home one hour	7.30 until 8.30 – work (incl. travel time)	7.30 to 5.45 + travel 40 mins Work home – 1hr	7.30 until 5.20. working. Travel home – 40 mins	7.30 until 5.40 incl. travel home.		
Total 11hrs 50	13 hrs	11 hrs 50	10hrs 30	10 hrs 10	NONE	NONE
				Grand Total 57hrs		20 mins

44

Michael's Maintenance Time Chart

	Mon	Tues	Wed	Thu	Fri	Sat	Sun
	7 – got up. Get ready – 20 mins Breakfast – 15 mins. Bed 10pm	6.30 – got up. Get ready – 1 hr. No evening meal (b⁄g) lunch. Bed 9pm	7 – got up. Get ready – 35 mins. Shopping in evening – 1 hr. Bed 9pm.	6.30 – 7.30 Get ready, go to work. Get ready to go out – 6.30 to 7.30pm. Bed 12am	7.00 – got up. Evening meal – 1 hr. Bed 10.30pm	9am – got up, bath. 10.30am lunch – 1½ hrs. Dinner – 1 hr. Bed 10.30pm	10.30 got up. Brunch! – 1 hr. Clean car – 1 hr. Cook + eat meal – 1¾. Bed 11pm.
Total	10 hrs 05.	9 hrs 30.	11 hrs 35.	11 hrs.	8 hrs.	14½ hrs.	16¾ hrs.
					Grand Total	81 hrs	25 mins

Michael's Discretionary Time Chart

	Mon	Tues	Wed	Thu	Fri	Sat	Sun
	Out for evening meal – 2 hrs.	T.V. – ½ hr.	Talked + drank at home – 1½ hr.	Went out for meal – 4½ hrs	Records – 1½ hrs. TV. Coffee – 1hr 20m. Guitar – 2 hrs Xmas cards – 1 hr 20 ms.	Buy Xmas tree – ½ hr. Buy gifts – 3 hrs. Assemble hi-fi – 1½ hrs. DIY – 4 hrs.	Xmas decorations + tea – 3 hrs. Make fire – ½ hr. Parents visit – 1½ hrs. Pub – 1½ hrs.
Total	2 hrs	½ hr	1½ hrs.	4½ hrs	6 hrs 10 ms.	9 hrs.	6½ hrs.
					Grand Total	30 hrs	10 mins

If you could compare your totals for Sold Time, Maintenance Time and Discretionary Time with those of other people you would find large variations. If possible, persuade some of your friends or colleagues to complete time charts so you can compare them.

People live their lives very differently. There is no right or wrong pattern. A mother of five will have a very different pattern from a retired single man. However, within individual patterns there is usually some room for manoeuvre. Where this is possible, most of us would choose to increase Discretionary Time because that is the time in which we can choose what to do. It is our leisure time.

Look over your three time charts. Are there any changes you can make in Sold and Mainte-nance Time to increase your Discretionary Time? Note down any ideas in the following space.

Changes I Could Make To Increase My Discretionary Time:

Summary

Any increase in Discretionary Time requires a reduction in Maintenance Time and Sold Time. We could choose to neglect our personal appearance to increase time for conversation and reading, but for most of us this would not be acceptable! One way of increasing Discretionary Time is by performing our sold and maintenance activities in shorter time, more efficiently.

The next section will help you identify Time Cheaters and Time Beaters. With the help of these you should have more time to do the things you want.

Section Nine: Time Cheaters and How to Stop Them

The objective of this section is to help you identify your Time Cheaters and find ways to beat them.

Time Cheaters come in all shapes and sizes; they can be physical and mental, created by you or imposed upon you by other people. The important thing is to become aware of them; then you can learn to deal with them.

Spend some time thinking about the things that stop or hinder you doing the things you want or need to do. Is there a neighbour or colleague who keeps you talking? Do you try to do too many things at the same time? Is your office or workroom disorganised? Write down any Time Cheaters that spring to mind.

```

```

You may find it difficult to identify your own particular Time Cheaters, or perhaps there were too many to mention! Look at the following list of Time Cheaters and for each one ask, 'Is this me?' If it is one of your Time Cheaters, tick the box and look at the possible solutions, or Time Beaters, that we've given.

Time Cheater	Is this me?	Time Beater
I spend too much time talking to people who won't go away?	☐	Learn to be firm, say 'I don't mean to be rude but I must get on with my work.'
I get side-tracked easily and lack self-discipline.	☐	Make Action Plans and *stick to them*. Promise yourself a reward for good time-keeping.

My colleagues/friends/kids interrupt me all the time.	☐	Tell everyone that you don't want to be disturbed. Have regular 'quiet' periods that people know about and recognise.
I take on too much work	☐	Learn to say 'No' politely but firmly. You may benefit from some assertiveness training: there's a book in this series called *Assertiveness: A Positive Process* which will help you.
Time runs out! I'm always rushed and late.	☐	Really think about what you have to do and how long it will take. Then add 20% extra time to form a time 'cushion'.
I get panicky and try to do everything at once.	☐	Prioritise! Spend five minutes quietly working out what jobs *must* be done and what can wait. Start at the top of your list and work through it steadily.
I spend ages looking for letters and files.	☐	You need to get organised. Read through Section Seven and start trying out different filing and sorting systems.

Summary

Can you think of any changes you can make, or action you can take, to prevent Time Cheaters? Write them down in the box below.

```



```

In the next section we introduce you to more ways of saving time.

Section Ten: Saving Time

The objective of this section is to discover ways of saving time.

As pointed out in Section Eight, we can increase Discretionary Time by saving time spent on our other activities. This leaves us more time to do the things we want. Alternatively, we could increase our workload without increasing Sold Time by performing work tasks more efficiently. Besides knowing what we want to do now and doing it, there is no simple rule for saving time. Effective time use comes from examining our activities and finding ways of excluding them or doing them more quickly.

Give yourself five minutes to write down all the ideas you can think of for saving time. At this stage, don't structure the ideas or evaluate them. If you can get someone else to share ideas with you, so much the better.

Personal Project

Now go back over your ideas and decide which you think are most useful. Write these into your planner, diary or file and work them into your planning activities.

Some Useful Time Beaters

Below are some time beaters that we have found useful; add your own at the end.

- Abolish waiting time! If you ever find yourself waiting for a bus, an appointment etc., don't think of it as a waste of time but think of it as a gift of time. Use it constructively. You could use it to relax, to weigh up a decision, to review your daily checklist, read a book, do the crossword – lots of things! Always carry pen and paper and a book to read.

- Make your daily checklists and prioritise. You are then less likely to spend time on C list activities.

- Make deadlines, write them in your diary and keep them.

- Combine activities, for examples, discussing a matter with your friend over lunch.

- Have a place for everything and keep everything in its place. If something's worth having, it's worth knowing where it is when you want it!

- Make yourself a filing system. You need something to contain the files – folders – and something to hold the folders – a large box or filing cabinet.

- Remember your first filing option is the waste paper basket. Do you really need that piece of paper? What is the worst thing that could happen if you didn't have it?

- Handle a piece of paper only once – deal with it the first time you pick it up.

- Always keep a notebook with you. Don't lose an idea because you had nowhere to record it. Think on paper.

- Reinforce your time-saving efforts. Reward yourself with something you really want when you have completed a task.

- If flexitime is available to you, use it to travel to work at off-peak times – save travelling time.

- Delegate as much as you can.

- Value your Discretionary Time at the same rate as your paid time. Is the time you spend travelling to a cheaper shop always worth the money saved?

- If you can afford a dishwasher, washing machine, microwave cooker or freezer – get one!

- Constantly ask yourself, 'Is this the best use of my time right now?'.

-
-
-
-

Now review your list. Put an X against all the ideas you find useful and list them in your planner.

Summary

You might be starting to feel that all the spontaneity has been planned out of your life! But you will have more time to take things as they come if you plan the things that you have to do. Time management aims to make you more relaxed and gives you more time to relax in.

Section Eleven: Leisure Time

The objective of this section is to help you identify your leisure needs and work out the activities which best meet them.

Earlier in this workbook we suggested that our time can be separated into Sold Time, Maintenance Time and Discretionary Time, and that Discretionary Time is the time available for us to choose what we do. Discretionary Time is the time available for leisure. In this section we look at this open-ended resource, how you choose to fill it and how to identify the many needs it can fill.

First let's look at the amount of time available to us as Discretionary Time. Is there any way of increasing it by cutting down on Sold Time and Maintenance Time? One way of dramatically altering the balance between Sold and Discretionary Time is to convert discretionary activities into sold activities, as musicians or professional athletes do, for example.

Even if you can't make a career of your hobby, there will be ways to increase Discretionary Time by a more ordered efficient approach to your sold and maintenance activities. Look back at Section Ten and then in the space overleaf jot down three ways in which you can increase your available Discretionary Time.

1 ....

2 ....

3 ....

After you have reduced your Sold and Maintenance Time as much as is practical, you will have expanded your Discretionary Time to its maximum in your present circumstances. The only way you can now increase your leisure satisfaction is by making choices. Your leisure cake is as big as it can be, you have now to decide what ingredients will make it the best possible cake for you. First, it would be useful to get a clear idea of what leisure means to you.

In the space below write as many definitions of leisure as you can think of in five minutes. Don't try to organise your ideas but let them flow freely. If you can get someone to do this with you so much the better.

Here are some definitions that occurred to us:

- Leisure is only attractive when we choose it.

- Leisure time includes play time, enjoyed for its own sake.

- Leisure time is time at your disposal after paid work and things like eating and sleeping (maintenance activities) have been done.

- Leisure time is recreation time. Time out from paid work to re-charge emotional, physical and intellectual batteries.

- Leisure and unemployment. We cannot ignore the concept of 'enforced leisure' and its attendant difficulties.

- Leisure time is positive time. You can exercise powerful choice in its use. You can enjoy it at whatever level you choose.

- Your choice of leisure activity is entirely individual; reasons for doing it are subjective and complex. For instance, playing tennis is a physical activity enjoyed for its sense of co-ordinated motion, until you get so good at it you are paid to do it. It is then a job. Playing tennis as an amateur can lead to meeting people, which makes it more a social pastime; although some people might use it as a chance to make business contacts.

An important point is that leisure time is pleasure time. It's not leisure if you didn't choose it. Enjoyment and choice are central to leisure.

What Do You Enjoy Most?

If you have a clear idea about what types of leisure activity you enjoy you will be in a better position to make choices between different activities. The questionnaire below is designed to help you identify the features of the leisure activity you enjoy most.

The Leisure Quotient Questionnaire which follows is arranged as a set of statements. Read each statement carefully and decide whether you agree or disagree with it. Indicate how far you agree or disagree with each statement by circling one of the numbers printed next to it.

1	2	3	4	5
Strongly disagree	Disagree	Not sure	Agree	Strongly agree

Leisure Quotient Questionnaire

Interests Group A: Being With People

1	2	3	4	5	I enjoy being in a crowd
1	2	3	4	5	I like talking to people
1	2	3	4	5	Who I'm with is more important than what I'm doing
1	2	3	4	5	I like joining clubs

Add up your score   Total =

Interests Group B: Being With Your Family

I	2	3	4	5	I like to plan family outings
I	2	3	4	5	I enjoy evenings when the family get together to talk and relax
I	2	3	4	5	I get on well with all generations in my family
I	2	3	4	5	I miss members of my family when we have to spend a long time apart

Add up your score   Total =

Interests Group C: Being Alone

I	2	3	4	5	I enjoy my own company
I	2	3	4	5	I like being able to concentrate on something without stopping to talk
I	2	3	4	5	I enjoy having a room or space of my own
I	2	3	4	5	I like to rely on my own judgment

Add up your score   Total =

Interests Group D: Using Your Brain

I	2	3	4	5	I enjoy time to think, plan and decide
I	2	3	4	5	I jump at an idea and like to follow it up for myself
I	2	3	4	5	I like reading and learning new facts
I	2	3	4	5	I enjoy discussing problems and issues

Add up your score   Total =

Interests Group E: Making Something

I	2	3	4	5	I like to see an end product for my efforts
I	2	3	4	5	I enjoy using my hands
I	2	3	4	5	I feel happy working with tools and machines
I	2	3	4	5	I like physical activity

Add up your score   Total =

Interests Group F: Helping Others

I	2	3	4	5	I like to feel useful
I	2	3	4	5	I like showing other people how to solve problems
I	2	3	4	5	I enjoy giving some of my time to good causes
I	2	3	4	5	I think we're here to make other people feel better

Add up your score   Total =

Interests Group G: Being Different

I	2	3	4	5	I like to stand out in a crowd
I	2	3	4	5	I enjoy doing the opposite to what people expect
I	2	3	4	5	I like to make up my own mind
I	2	3	4	5	I like exploring new ways of doing things

Add up your score   Total =

Interests Group H: Taking Exercise

I	2	3	4	5	I like to be very fit
I	2	3	4	5	I enjoy physical activity
I	2	3	4	5	I like being outdoors
I	2	3	4	5	I like to meet a hard physical challenge

Add up your score   Total =

Interests Group I: Being Creative

I	2	3	4	5	I like to use my imagination
I	2	3	4	5	I like to express myself through painting or music or writing (score for any of these)
I	2	3	4	5	I like to daydream
I	2	3	4	5	I like being in an atmosphere where people are using their imaginations

Add up your score   Total =

Interests Group J: Competing With Others

1	2	3	4	5	I get a kick out of winning
1	2	3	4	5	I like to do things to the best of my ability
1	2	3	4	5	I like to find out if I can do things better than other people
1	2	3	4	5	Second isn't good enough

Add up your score   Total =

Interests Group K: Appreciating Nature

1	2	3	4	5	I prefer to be in open spaces to being in towns
1	2	3	4	5	I enjoy seeing beautiful scenery
1	2	3	4	5	I like to learn about nature from books and TV programmes
1	2	3	4	5	I like animals and plants

Add up your score   Total =

Interests Group L: Escaping From Stress

1	2	3	4	5	I like to find a way to 'wind down' after work
1	2	3	4	5	I like things that take my attention off problems
1	2	3	4	5	I like to take off on the spur of the moment and do something unexpected
1	2	3	4	5	Relaxing is as important as working

Add up your score   Total =

Interests Group M: Being Entertained

1	2	3	4	5	I like being a member of an audience
1	2	3	4	5	I like looking out for events that I can go to
1	2	3	4	5	I like sitting back and being taken out of myself by a sports event, a concert, film or play or something on television
1	2	3	4	5	I like talking about an event I've enjoyed

Add up your score   Total =

Add up your scores for each interests group. Now rank your groups in order, putting the interest group with the highest score first, and so on.

Order	Group letter	Score
1.		
2.		
3.		
4.		
5.		
6.		
7.		
8.		
9.		
10.		
11.		
12.		
13.		

Draw a line under the first three groups. These are your main leisure types.

If you score high in groups:
A B C F G I J K L M
Look at leisure activities to meet your emotional and social needs – how you feel and how you relate to others.

If you score high in groups:
E H K L
Look at activities geared to your physical needs – how your body feels.

If you score high in groups:
C D E I M
Look at activities that satisfy intellectual needs – things which stimulate your mind.

Are you surprised by your leisure needs as shown by your Leisure Quotient Questionnaire?

Each of the three leisure types will have their own type of leisure activities that suits them best. Below is a list of activities corresponding to each group. Take your three highest scoring groups and look at the activities suggested for each of these groups on the Loadsa Leisure! table.

Loadsa Leisure!

Group A – Being With People

Card games	Golf	Zoos	Football
Pub	Museums	Dancing	Badminton
Camping	Art Class	Night School	Eating Out
Tennis	Snooker	Cinema	
Theatre	Amusements	Parks	

Group B – Being With Your Family

Bicycling	Camping	Pub	Cooking
Model Making	Stamp Collecting	Holidays	T.V.
Jigsaws	Fishing	Boating	
Reading	Board Games	Table Tennis	

Group C – Being Alone

Sightseeing	Crosswords	Sewing	Writing
Photography	Woodwork	Jogging	Stereo
Reading	Meditation	Collecting Dolls	
Coins/Antiques	Bird Watching	Painting	
T.V.	Swimming	Music	

Group D – Using Your Mind

Travel	Reading	Flying	Museums
Night School	Astronomy	Art Galleries	
Chess	Sailing	Genealogy	
Archaeology	Lectures	Book Club	

Group E – Making Something

Sculpture	Gardening	Macramé	Photography
Nature Collections	Knitting	Wine Making	Painting
Restoring Antiques	Weaving	Decorating	Writing
Making Models	Leather Craft	Woodwork	

Group F – Helping Others

Babysitting	Meals on Wheels	Jumble Sales	Volunteer Work
Entertaining	Massage	Sponsored Events	Tarot Reading

Group G – Being Different

(Female) Football	Skydiving	Sewing (Male)	Rock Climbing
Hang Gliding	Mechanics (Female)	Cooking (Male)	

Group H – Taking Exercise

Gym	Yoga	Cross-Country	Racquet Sports
Ice Skating	Athletics	Swimming	Riding
Soccer	Dancing	Cycling	Volleyball
Calisthenics	Canoeing	Jogging	

Group I – Being Creative

Modelmaking	Scrapbook	Woodwork	Music
Dance	Needlework	Restoring Furniture	Clothes Design
Drama	Weaving	Flower Arranging	Writing
Sketching	Photography	Baking	

Group J – Competing With Others

Chess	Rounders	Board Games	Dance Contests
Golf	Bowling	Archery	Racing
Card Games	Boxing	Tennis	Exhibiting Animals
Basketball	Soccer	Athletics	

Group K – Appreciating Nature

Zoos	Archaeology	Rock Climbing	Fishing
Hill Climbing	Riding	Astronomy	Gardening
Walking	Beachcombing	Sailing	Landscaping
Geology	Camping	Sketching	Nature Programmes

Group L – Escaping From Stress			
Cinema	Painting	Having a Bath	Puzzles
Squash	Jogging	Parks	Walking
Fair	Travel	Reading	Pub
Sunbathing	Radio	T.V.	

Group M – Being Entertained			
T.V.	Films	Reading	Travel
Magazines	Concerts	Conversation	
Spectator Sports	Music	Theatre	
Folk Clubs	Ballet	Circus	

Explore each of the activities listed in your three highest scoring groups. Use the chart below to evaluate them, by weighing up the advantages and disadvantages of each for you. This offers you the opportunity to consider new leisure activities suited to your leisure type which you might not have thought about before.

Leisure activity	Advantages	Disadvantages

Section Eleven: Leisure Time

Here is an example of one person's chart:

Leisure activity	Advantages	Disadvantages
Archery	New skill. Outdoor activity. Meet new people. Romantic. Can hire gear.	Cost of equipment. Travelling time. Dangerous. Never done it before.
Card games.	Exercise. Win money. Meet people. Play anywhere.	I always lose. I gamble recklessly. Boring. Gets in the way of talking. Don't like sitting still !

Look over your chart and circle the new activities where the advantages outweigh the disadvantages. Include these new leisure activities into planning your discretionary time. Look carefully at your stated disadvantages. Words like boring and taking too much time often conceal more accurate reasons which we don't like to admit to ourselves. For example, saying something is boring often conceals that we don't have the skills to do it successfully. If we acknowledge we don't have the skills we are in a position to set about acquiring them.

In the space below write down a list of ten things you enjoy doing.

How I can start doing more .... now.

....

....

How I can start doing more .... now.

....

....

How I can start doing more .... now.

....

....

Another way to open out your leisure choices is to use the What's On guide and adverts in your local paper. Buy a paper, go through it and underline activities you have not done before and would quite like to do. You could also try the main and local libraries or community centres, as they usually have details about what's going on in your area. Set yourself a target to do one new thing each week for the next four weeks. Write these new activities into your monthly plan.

Four things to do or see in the next month:

....

....

....

....

Summary

In this section you have identified your own leisure needs and explored new choices for your leisure. You have acquired the skills and techniques for evaluating these new leisure activities throughout this programme. Given that your Discretionary Time is limited, you will have to choose between your leisure activities, both new and old. As always prioritising activities is our guide to making the best of your leisure time.

In the space below list your leisure choices for next week and prioritise them.

....

....

....

....

....

....

When you've done this, fit in your leisure priorities alongside the other activities in your diary.

Section Twelve: Programme Review

The objective of this section is to review your gains from time management.

Time management means organising yourself better to get out of your time what *you* want. Its aim is not to fill up your life with activity! It is to help you to identify what you want out of life and to plan how to go about getting it; so you know what to do to achieve what you want in life. You have been introduced to, and used, a number of techniques to achieve this. This is a good time to re-evaluate these techniques.

Run down the list of techniques which you have used in the programme. Think about whether or not the techniques worked for you, jot down why you found them successful or why you think they didn't suit you.

Time Investment Techniques

Life Investment Record (page 13)

....

....

Activity Charts (pages 14–15)

....

....

Satisfaction and Time Pie Comparisons (pages 22–23)

....

....

Use of Time, Priority Chart (page 28)

....

....

List Making (page 30)

....

....

List Prioritising (page 31)

....

....

Using a Diary (page 34)

....

....

Using a Planner (page 34)

....

....

Creating Efficient Working Environment (page 38)

....

....

Time Cheaters (page 47)

....

....

Time Beaters (page 50)

....

....

Final Comment: Time Management NOW

We hope you have enjoyed working through this book, and that you have achieved what you wanted from it.

Look back at your personal objectives (on page 11) and the question we asked you just before them. Has your thinking changed since then? If it has, jot down your new ideas about time in the following space.

....

....

....

....

Now is a good time to review what you have gained, and start applying it!

In the space below, list three things you have learnt about yourself and the way you manage your time as a result of this workbook.

1 ....

2 ....

3 ....

Now list three things to improve the way you manage your time that you have learnt as a result of doing this workbook.

1 ....

2 ....

3 ....

Remember the skill is not to make a plan and stick to it but to make a plan and constantly ask the question: is it working? If not, it's time to revise the plan.

Try to set some space aside every month to review how you are using your time – write it in your planner to make sure you make time!

You have now reached the end of this time management workbook – you should be ready to conquer the clock! You may find that you need to refresh your memory from time to time; just go over some of the sections you found most useful. We hope that you have enjoyed this book and that you will have fun putting your new skills into action.

'To Choose Time Is To Save Time.'

Francis Bacon

Lifeskills

Personal Development Series

Other titles available in this series are:

ASSERTIVENESS:
A Positive Process

'When we are assertive, we tell people what we want or need or would prefer. We state ou[r] preferences clearly and confidently, without being aggressive, without belittling ourselves an[d] without putting other people down.' Most of us are capable of being assertive, aggressive or unassertive at different times. The aim of this book is to help you benefit from the positive process of being assertive as consistently as you can. *Assertiveness: A Positive Process* will:

- help you to distinguish between assertive, aggressive and unassertive behaviour

- ensure that you understand the benefits of being assertive – and the dilemmas

- introduce you to some helpful techniques for dealing with people assertively.

COMMUNICATION:
Time to Talk

'It is tempting to assume that our communication skills come to us as part of our natural development. Yet some people develop into very effective communicators, while others barely reach survival level.' Without communication there would be no relationships between people; sharing ideas, giving opinions, finding out what we need to know, working out differences, giving positive criticism and expressing our feelings are examples of the kind of face-to-face communication which is essential to our everyday life and work with other people. *Time to Talk* will:

- explain how to recognise and prevent 'communication breakdown' at work and at home
- help you to identify helpful and unhelpful ways of communicating
- encourage you to develop and improve your interpersonal communication skills.

TRANSITIONS:
The Challenge of Change

'When a chrysalis metamorphoses into a butterfly it is a natural process, it is something that must happen for the insect to become beautiful, to fly, to mate, to realise its potential.' This is a good symbol to use about facing our own transitions, because we need to change to realise our potential. Change is essential and creates opportunities, but it often causes stress and worry. Modern life is full of changes; the list is endless. *The Challenge of Change* will:

- help you to identify the different types of transition and their patterns
- help you make sense of the confusing feelings you may experience after an upheaval
- emphasise the benefits that can come from transitions, and provide a step-by-step, comprehensive guide to managing change positively.

Other Mercury titles from Lifeskills are:

BUILD YOUR OWN RAINBOW
Barrie Hopson and Mike Scally

A Lifeskills Workbook for Career and Life Management

Adopted by the Open University for Work Choices, a Community Education course.

Build Your Own Rainbow is the first of a new series of Lifeskills guides. It contains 40 exercises that will help answer the questions:

- who am I?
- where am I now?
- how satisfied am I?
- what changes do I want?
- how do I make them happen?
- what if it doesn't work out?

In the process of doing this, readers will discover what is important to them about work, where their main interests lie, what their transferable skills are and which career pattern would best suit them. They will be helped to set personal and career objectives, to make action plans and to take greater charge of their lives.

12 STEPS TO SUCCESS THROUGH SERVICE
Barrie Hopson and Mike Scally

A Lifeskills Management Guide

Satisfying the customer is the single most vital factor in business success and the main priority in any business must be to win and keep the customer. This book provides a complete programme to achieve success through service in twelve crucial steps:

- decide on your core business
- know your customer
- create your wisdom
- define your moments of truth
- give good service to one another
- manage the customer's experience
- profit from complaints
- stay close to your customer
- design and market the service programme
- set service criteria
- reward service excellence
- develop the service programme.

Lifeskills is one of the leading providers of Quality Service Programmes in the English-speaking world.

POSITIVE LEADERSHIP
Mike Pegg

How to Build a Winning Team
A Lifeskills Management Guide

Good leaders have many features in common. They develop a clear vision, they inspire their people, gain commitment from them, then guide their teams to success. This sounds easy in theory, but how is it done?

This is a book written for top teams, managers, and anybody who is a leader of people. It offers a framework for leadership and teamwork, with concrete ideas which can be incorporated into the daily work plan.

If focuses on how to:

- provide positive leadership
- be a positive team member
- build a positive culture
- set a positive goal, and get commitment to reaching it
- be a positive implementer
- build a positive reputation
- get positive results
- continue to build a positive and successful team.

69

Notes

Notes

Notes